Bastien® New Traditions

All In One
PIANO COURSE

BY LISA, LORI, & JANE BASTIEN

Level
LESSONS
THEORY
TECHNIC
PERFORMANCE

Illustrations by **Ying-Hwa Hu**

ISBN-10: 0-8497-9787-X
ISBN-13: 978-0-8497-9787-3

Dear Teachers and Parents:

Bastien New Traditions: All In One Piano Course is a captivating and dynamic method designed for student achievement and success. It combines the successful, time-tested Bastien piano pedagogy with new teaching ideas and techniques. Stemming from our many years of experience teaching students of diverse abilities and interests, we have developed this engaging curriculum for today's busy students.

Features include:

- **All-in-one books** with lesson, technic, theory, and performance pages fully integrated in each book for a streamlined, comprehensive, easy-to-use approach.

- **Appropriate reinforcement** and pacing throughout to ensure success for students with diverse abilities and interests.

- **Innovative, gradual multi-key** approach blended with intervallic reading. Staff reading begins with Middle C using varied hand placements, as well as traditional 5-finger positions.

- **Captivating music**, featuring outstanding solo pieces and duet accompaniments, an excellent variety of different musical styles, and an abundance of familiar melodies to inspire students.

- **Holistic approach** to concepts integrating elements of lessons, theory, technic, and performance.

- **Inviting pages**, beautifully organized and clutter-free, with stunning watercolor illustrations.

- **Technology** included in every book designed to assist practice and motivate students.

Learning to play the piano is an enriching and joyful experience. We wish you much success in your student's musical journey!

Neil A. Kjos Music Company
Lisa Bastien
Lori Bastien
Jane Smisor Bastien

Essential Supplementary Materials for Level 1A:

Bastien Assignment Book (KP50)

Rhythm $\frac{2}{4}, \frac{3}{4}, \frac{4}{4}$ (KP30)

Bastien Music Flashcards (GP27) The daily use of music flashcards is highly recommended to aid in recognizing individual notes. Each time new notes are introduced, numbered miniature flashcards are included on the page. These numbers correspond with the Bastien *Music Flashcards* (GP27). Find and separate the numbered cards from your set of music flashcards. Name, play, and memorize these new notes.

Contents

WP452

REFERENCE and REVIEW

The Grand Staff

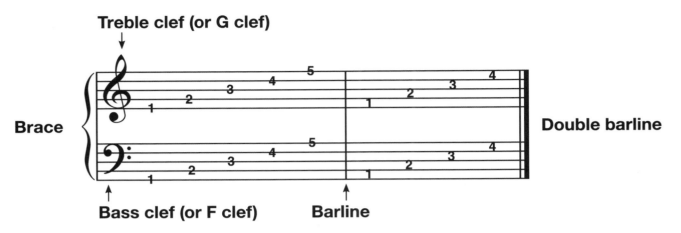

Treble clef (or G clef)

Brace

Double barline

Bass clef (or F clef)   **Barline**

The Notes on the Staff and Keyboard

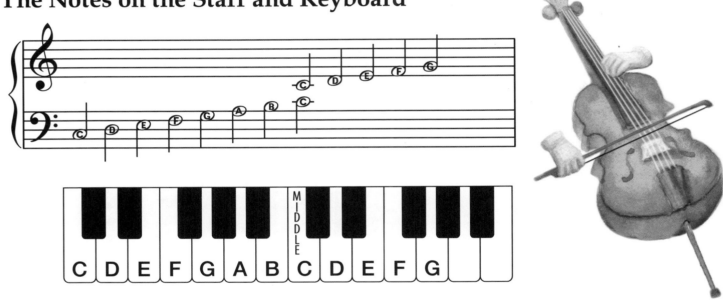

Time Signatures

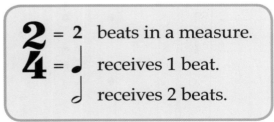

2/4 = **2** beats in a measure.
= ♩ receives 1 beat.
= ♩ receives 2 beats.

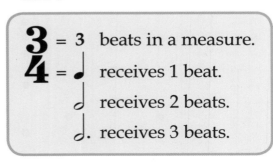

3/4 = **3** beats in a measure.
= ♩ receives 1 beat.
= ♩ receives 2 beats.
= ♩. receives 3 beats.

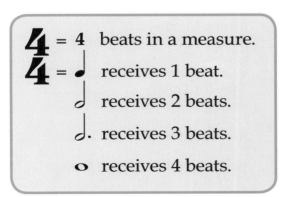

4/4 = **4** beats in a measure.
= ♩ receives 1 beat.
= ♩ receives 2 beats.
= ♩. receives 3 beats.
= o receives 4 beats.

Notes and Rests

	Quarter 1 beat	Half 2 beats	Dotted Half 3 beats	Whole 4 beats
Note:	♩	♩	♩.	o
Rest:	⌐	▬		
Count:	1	1 - 2	1 - 2 - 3	1 - 2 - 3 - 4

Whole Rest

▬

A whole rest is a whole measure of silence:

$\frac{2}{4}$ ▬ = 2 beats $\frac{3}{4}$ ▬ = 3 beats $\frac{4}{4}$ ▬ = 4 beats

Intervals

2nd (Step)

line – space   space – line

3rd (Skip)

line – line   space – space

Signs and Terms

Sign	Italian Name	Meaning
p	*piano*	soft
mp	*mezzo piano*	medium soft
mf	*mezzo forte*	medium loud
f	*forte*	loud
:‖		repeat
D. C. al Fine	*(Da Capo al Fine)*	go back to the beginning of the piece and play to the *Fine*.
8*va*		play one octave higher or lower

C 5-Finger Position

Penguins on Parade

Happily

mf Pen-guins on pa- rade to- day, see them wob-ble as they play.

You are ready for **Rhythm** $\frac{2}{4}$, $\frac{3}{4}$, $\frac{4}{4}$ (KP30).

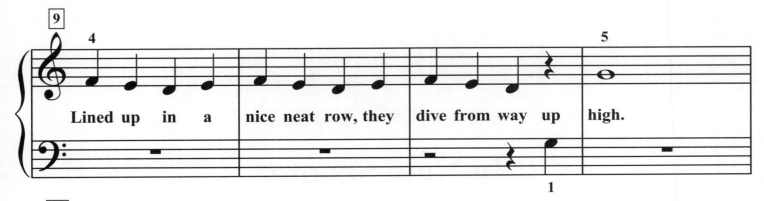

9

Lined up in a | nice neat row, they | dive from way up | high.

13

Splash! They land be- | neath the waves, these | birds who swim, not | fly!

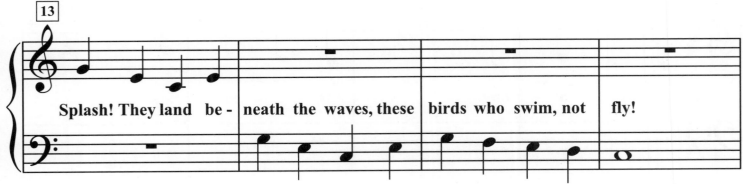

17

mp Pen - guins | on pa-rade, | pen-guins on pa- | rade! *p*

Optional damper pedal

Slur = Legato

A **slur** is a curved line over or under two or more *different* notes that are to be played **legato** (smooth and connected).

The slur is also used to show a musical thought called a **phrase**.

Lift your hand gently at the end of a slur or phrase.

RH 1 begins on ___.
LH 1 begins on ___.

My New Scooter

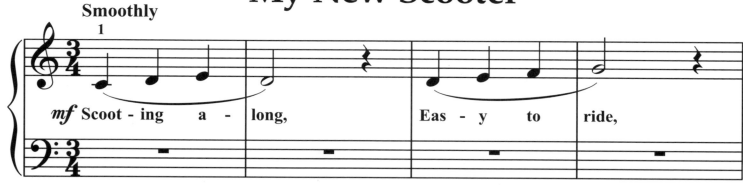

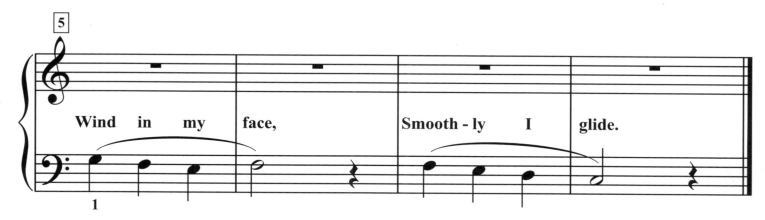

Tie = Hold

A **tie** is a curved line that connects notes on the *same* line or space. Play the first note only and hold it for the value of both notes.

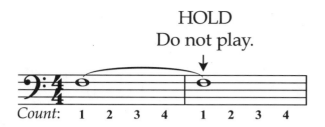

HOLD
Do not play.

Count: 1 2 3 4 1 2 3 4

LH 2 begins on ____.

All Through the Night

Moderately

Welsh Lullaby

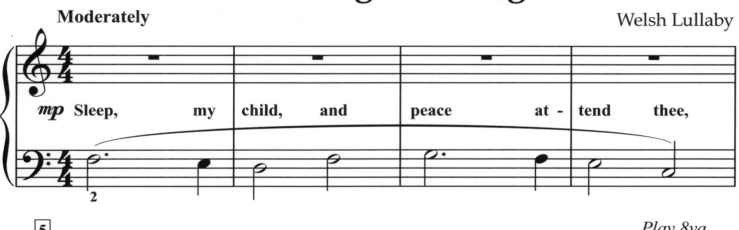

mp Sleep, my child, and peace at - tend thee,

5

Play 8va higher on repeat

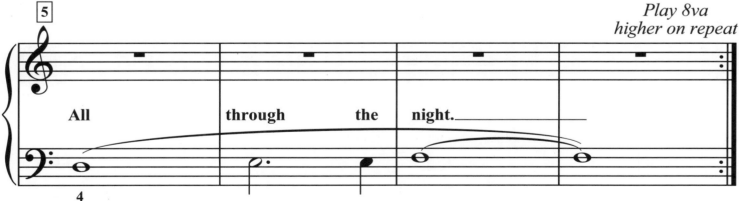

All through the night._____

ACCOMPANIMENT (Student plays one octave higher.)

p legato

WP452

1. Write the counts under the rhythm.
2. Clap and count it aloud.

RH 3 begins on ___.
LH 2 begins on ___.

Shoo Fly

T. Brigham Bishop

Brightly

mf Shoo fly,___ don't both-er me! Shoo fly,___ don't both-er me!

Shoo fly,___ don't both-er me, for I be-long to some-bo- dy.

ACCOMPANIMENT (Student plays one octave higher.)

mp staccato

Time for Theory

A. Circle the correct answer.

slur
tie

slur
tie

slurs
ties

slurs
ties

B. Name each note, then place its number on the matching key below.

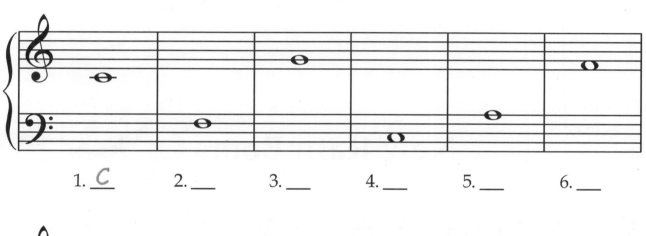

1. _C_   2. ___   3. ___   4. ___   5. ___   6. ___

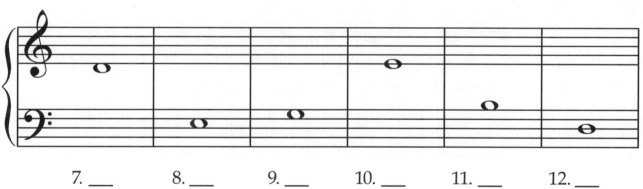

7. ___   8. ___   9. ___   10. ___   11. ___   12. ___

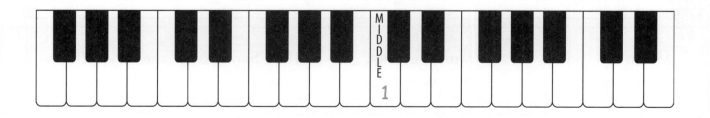

Harmonic Intervals

Harmonic intervals are two notes played together to make harmony in music.

2nd   3rd

Name the notes, then circle the name of the harmonic interval.

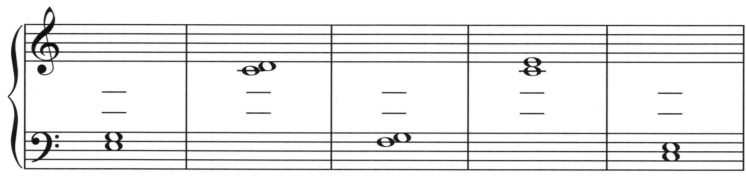

2nd or 3rd   2nd or 3rd   2nd or 3rd   2nd or 3rd   2nd or 3rd

RH 1 begins on ___.
LH 1 begins on ___.

New Rain Boots

Moderately

mf 1. New   rain   boots!   Love them   so!   Out   I   go!
mp 2. Splish, splish, splash!   Run   and   jump!   Love   to   play!

When   it   pours   from   the   sky,   Rain boots keep   me   dry!
Stay   out - side   all   day   long   On   a   rain - y   day!

Melodic Intervals

Melodic intervals are single notes played one at a time, like notes in a melody.

2nd   3rd

Name the notes, then circle the name of the melodic intervals.

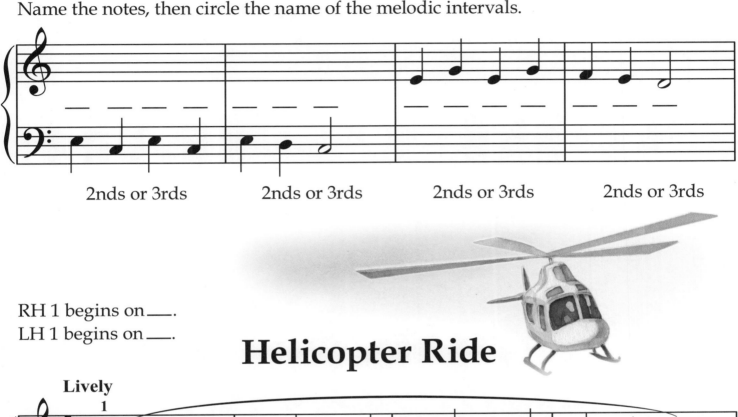

2nds or 3rds   2nds or 3rds   2nds or 3rds   2nds or 3rds

RH 1 begins on ___.
LH 1 begins on ___.

Helicopter Ride

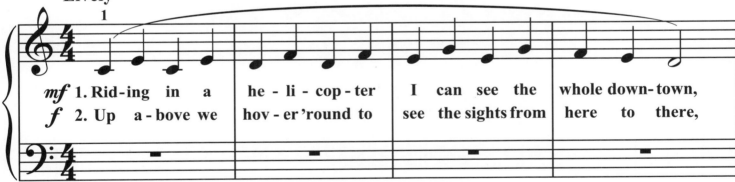

Lively

mf 1. Rid-ing in a   he - li - cop - ter   I can see the   whole down-town,
f 2. Up a - bove we   hov - er 'round to   see the sights from   here to there,

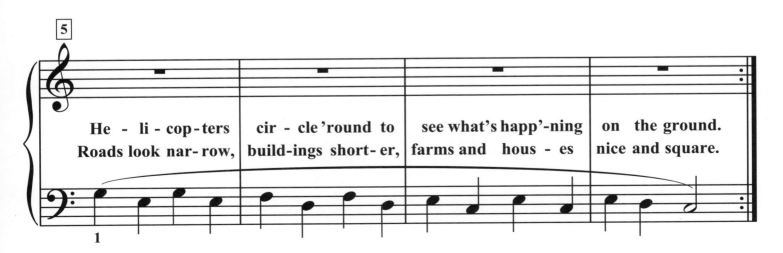

He - li - cop - ters   cir - cle 'round to   see what's happ'-ning   on the ground.
Roads look nar- row,   build-ings short- er,   farms and hous - es   nice and square.

Interval of a 4th

A **4th** is written:

from a **line note to a space note**   OR   from a **space note to a line note**.

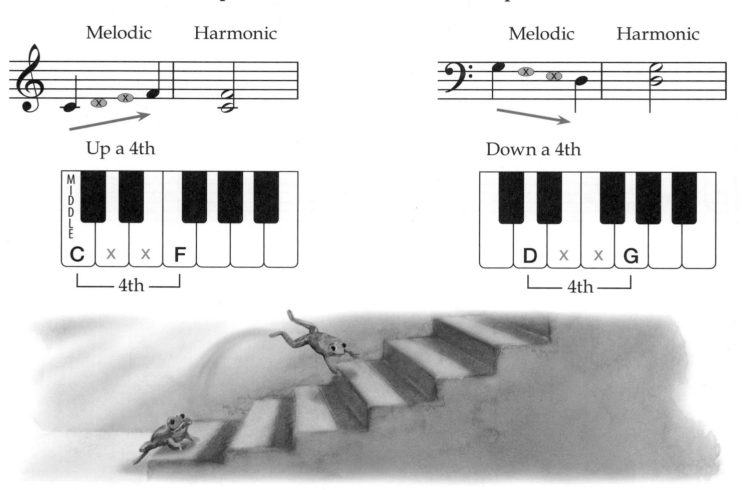

Name the notes, then circle the correct interval.

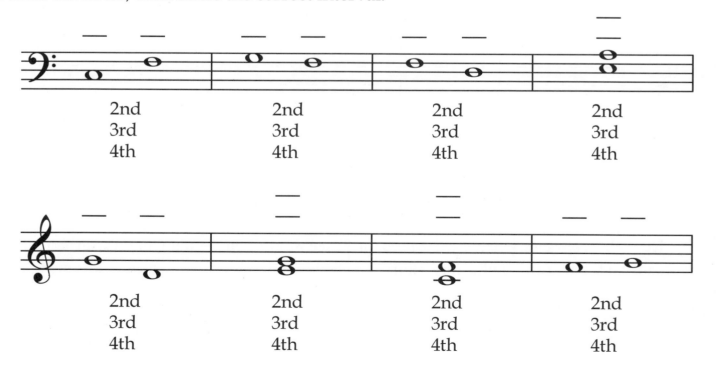

2nd	2nd	2nd	2nd
3rd	3rd	3rd	3rd
4th	4th	4th	4th

2nd	2nd	2nd	2nd
3rd	3rd	3rd	3rd
4th	4th	4th	4th

RH 4 begins on ___.
RH 1 begins on ___.

LH 2 begins on ___.
LH 5 begins on ___.

Bell Tower

Brightly

*Optional pedal

LH 4 begins on ___.
RH 1 begins on ___.

Down in the Valley

American Folk Song

Moderately

mf

1. Down in the val - ley, val - ley so low,___
2. Hear the wind blow dear, hear the wind blow,___

Hang your head o - ver, hear the wind blow.___
Hang your head o - ver, hear the wind blow.___

ACCOMPANIMENT (Student plays one octave higher.)

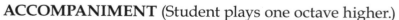

p   *legato*

Tempo Marks

Tempo marks are placed at the beginning of a piece to tell the rate of speed at which the piece is to be played. Tempo marks are usually in Italian.

Selected tempo marks, listed from slow to fast:

Andante	slowly (walking tempo)
Moderato	moderately
Allegretto	moderately fast
Allegro	fast

LH 5 begins on ___.
RH 1 begins on ___.

Aura Lee

American Folk Song

ACCOMPANIMENT (Student plays one octave higher.)

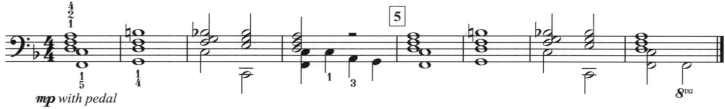

mp with pedal

Interval of a 5th

A **5th** is written:

from a **line note to a line note**   OR   from a **space note to a space note**.

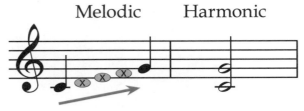

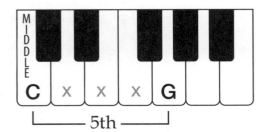

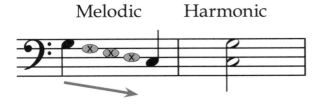

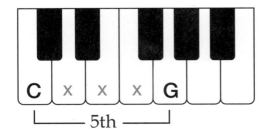

Name the notes, then write the interval name (**2nd, 3rd, 4th, 5th**) in the box.

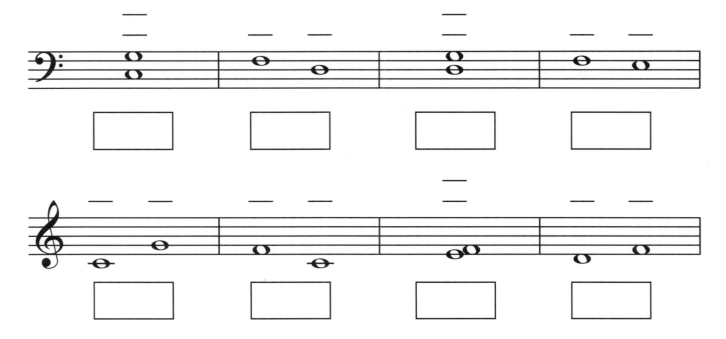

Review

Draw three half rests. Remember, the half rest (▬) sits on the 3rd staff line.

▬ = 2 beats of silence

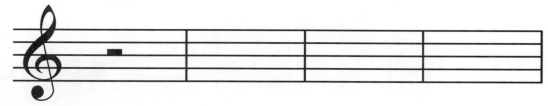

Draw three whole rests. Remember, the whole rest (▬) hangs down from the 4th staff line.

▬ = a whole measure of silence

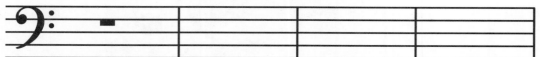

RH 1 begins on ___.
LH 2 begins on ___.

Star Gazing

Andante

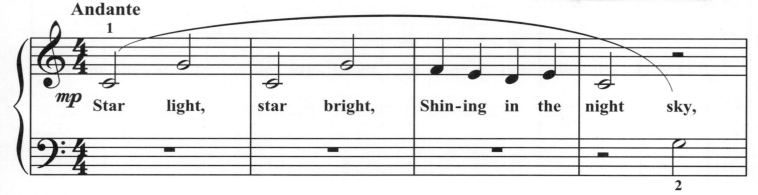

Star light, star bright, Shin-ing in the night sky,

Star light, star bright, Shine for me to - night.

ACCOMPANIMENT (Student plays one octave higher.)

with pedal

LH 5 begins on ___.
RH 1 begins on ___.

Sleepy Puppy

French Folk Tune

Andante

Sleep-y pup-py, sleep-y pup-py, Please wake up! Please wake up!

We will run and play all day. Please wake up! Sleep-y pup!

ACCOMPANIMENT (Student plays one octave higher.)

RH 1 begins on ___.
LH 1 begins on ___.

Picking Apples

Moderato

f Ap - ple sea - son | comes in fall, the | ap - ples are so | tast - y,

Pick - ing ap - ples | off the trees, each | one so fresh and | juic - y.

Harmony for Two

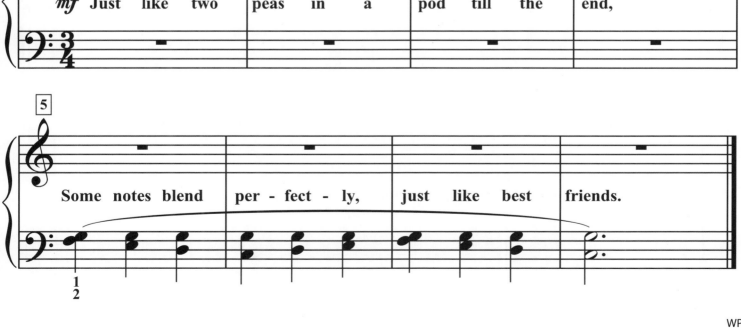

Andante

mf Just like two | peas in a | pod till the | end,

Some notes blend | per - fect - ly, | just like best | friends.

Staccato

Staccato means to play short, separated notes.

A dot over 𝅗𝅥 or under 𝅘𝅥 a note means to play it staccato.

RH 1 begins on ___.
LH 1 begins on ___.

Raindrops

Moderato

mf Pit - ter   pat - ter,   lis - ten to the   rain!

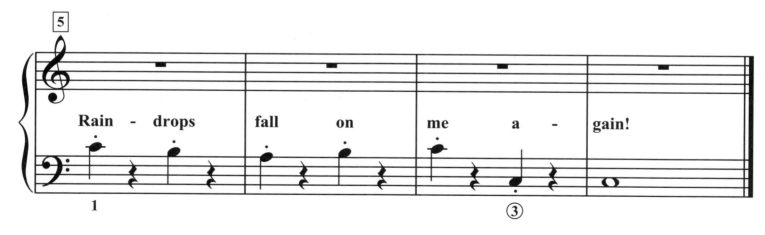

Rain - drops   fall   on   me a -   gain!

ACCOMPANIMENT (Student plays one octave higher.)

mp

Trace the quarter rest (𝄽), then draw three more.

Remember,
𝄽 = 1 beat
of silence

RH 1 begins on ___.
LH 1 begins on ___.

Popcorn Time!

Moderato

mf Pop-corn time, | fresh and light, | pop it up | Fri - day night!

Pop-corn time, | mov - ie night, | pop it up, | just right!

ACCOMPANIMENT (Student plays one octave higher.)

mp

WP452

𝄞 Space A

Draw three A's.

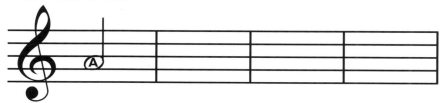

Ritardando (*rit.*) means gradually slow down.

Name the notes.

New Note

30

LH 5 begins on ____.
RH 1 begins on ____.

Skating on the Lake

Allegretto

1   LH over   RH **5**

mf Win - ter ar - rives o - ver - night,   seems that the

Optional pedal

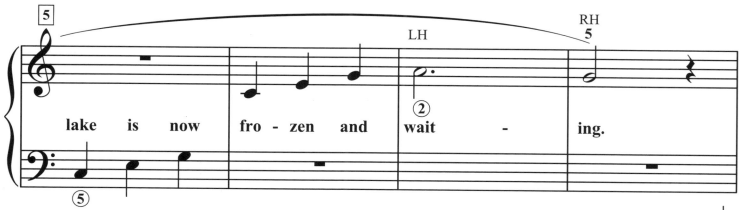

5

LH   RH 5

lake is now   fro - zen and   wait -   ing.

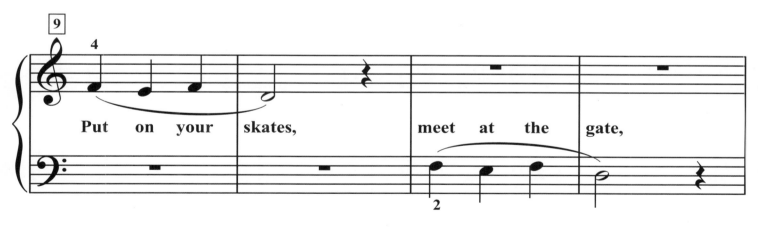

9

Put on your skates, meet at the gate,

13

*Play both hands
8va higher on repeat*

Ice skat - ing out on the lake!

rit. (2nd time)

mp

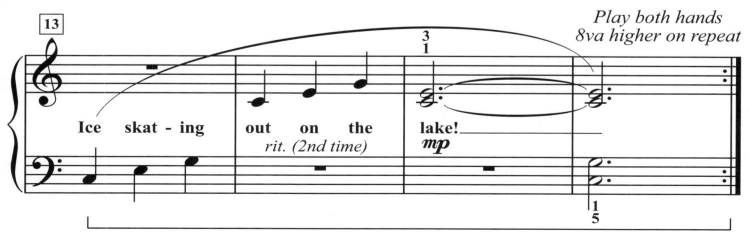

RH 1 begins on ___.
LH 2 begins on ___.

Pop! Goes the Weasel

English Folk Song

ACCOMPANIMENT (Student plays one octave higher.)

Music Math

A. In **4/4** :

♩ = __ beats   𝅝 = __ beats

𝄼 = __ beats   ▬ = __ beats

♩. = __ beats   ♪ = __ beat

𝄽 = __ beat

B. Complete these "music math" problems. Remember, a whole rest (▬) means a whole measure of silence.

In **4/4** : ♩ = ☐
    𝄽 = ☐
    𝄼 = ☐
+ ▬ = ☐
Total = ☐

In **3/4** : 𝅗𝅥. = ☐
    ▬ = ☐
    𝄽 = ☐
+ ♪ = ☐
Total = ☐

In **2/4** : 𝄽 = ☐
    ♪ = ☐
    ▬ = ☐
+ 𝄽 = ☐
Total = ☐

C. Add notes or rests to complete these measures. Clap and count the rhythm aloud.

3/4 ☐ | ☐ | ☐ | ☐ ‖

         rest   note   note   rest

2/4 ☐ | | ☐ | ☐  ‖

         note   rest   note

♭ = Flat Sign

A **flat sign** (♭) before a note means to play the nearest key to the left.
The nearest key may be a black key or a white key.

 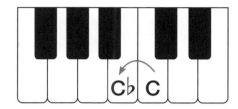 

Matching

Draw lines connecting each staff note to its matching key on the keyboard.

 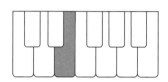 

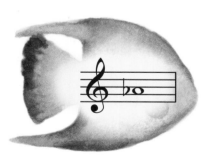 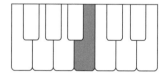

  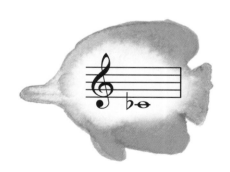

LH 1 begins on ___.
LH 5 begins on ___.

RH 5 begins on ___.
RH 1 begins on ___.

Mountain Drums

Moderato

mf

8va

5

Drums are sound-ing   far a-way,   Hear their stead-y   beat.

9

Peace-ful, dis-tant   moun-tain drums,   Lull-ing me to   sleep!

13

mp   *p*

8va

*Shade the correct key.

Flat Sign (♭) Practice

A. 1. A flat (♭) means to play the nearest key to the left / right.

   (Circle one.)

   2. A note with a flat may be a black *or* white key. True or False

   (Circle one.)

   3. Draw three flat signs: ___ ___ ___

B. Trace the flat sign in front of each note, then shade the matching key.

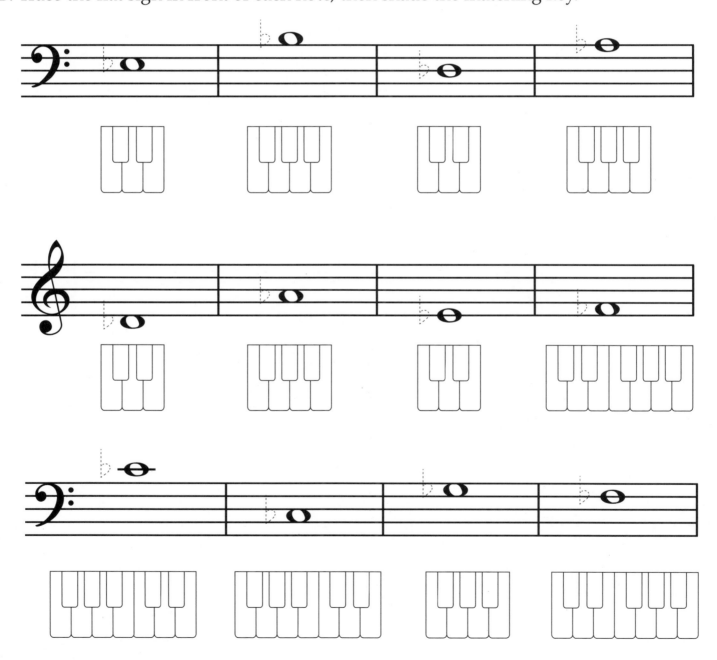

> ♭ = **Flat Sign**
> A flat note remains flat for a whole measure.
>
> also D♭

RH 3 begins on ___.
LH 2 begins on ___.

Market Treasures

also D♭

Moderato

f 1. Ped-dlers sell their trea - sures   in an o - pen mar - ket
p 2. Coins of gold and sil - ver,   box - es filled with ru - bies

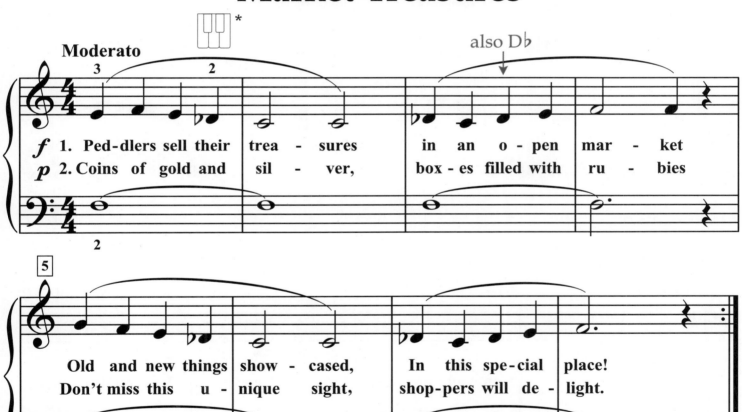

Old and new things show - cased,   In this spe - cial place!
Don't miss this u - nique sight,   shop-pers will de - light.

*Shade the correct key.

ACCOMPANIMENT (Student plays one octave higher.)

1., 2., 3.   4.

mf *(first verse)*
pp *2nd repeat (second verse)*

WP452

♯ = Sharp Sign

A **sharp sign** (♯) before a note means to play the nearest key to the right. The nearest key may be a black key or a white key.

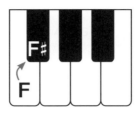
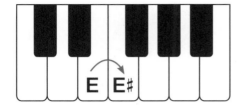

Matching

Draw lines connecting each staff note to its matching key on the keyboard.

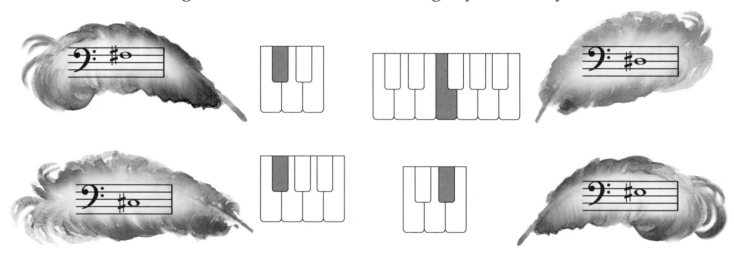

LH 4 begins on ___.
RH 1 begins on ___.

Can-Can

Allegro

Jacques Offenbach

f Hey! | Can you do the | Can   Can? | I know that you

ACCOMPANIMENT (Student plays one octave higher.)

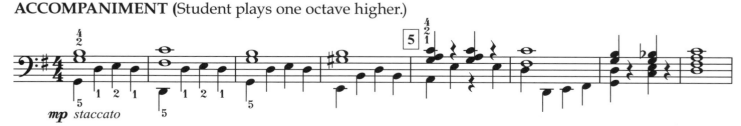

mp *staccato*

*Shade the correct key.

Sharp Sign (♯) Practice

A. 1. A sharp (♯) means to play the nearest key to the left / right.

(Circle one.)

2. A note with a sharp may be a black *or* white key. True or False

(Circle one.)

3. Draw three sharp signs: __ __ __

B. Trace the sharp sign in front of each note, then shade the matching key.

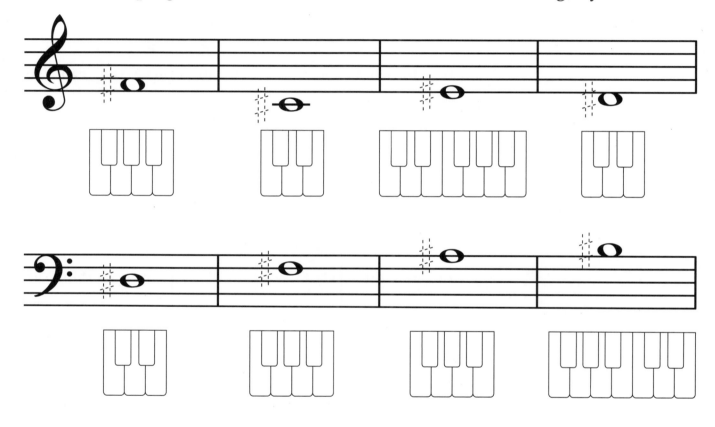

Reading In My Hammock

ACCOMPANIMENT (Student plays one octave higher.**)**

LH 2 begins on ___.
RH 1 begins on ___.

Reading In My Hammock

Andante
mp
1. In my ham-mock I can read. Un-der-neath a sha-ded tree,
2. Af-ter school I love to play, Then I grab my book. Hoo-ray!
legato
Fine
Lose my-self in-side my book, so peace-ful-ly.
Read-ing in my ham-mock on a bright, clear day!
p
D.C. al Fine

Upbeats

Count: 3   4   1   2   3   4

Notes that come before the first full measure of a piece are called **upbeats**. Usually the time value of the upbeats is taken away from the final measure, making that measure incomplete. The beats in the first measure plus the beats in the last measure equal one full measure.

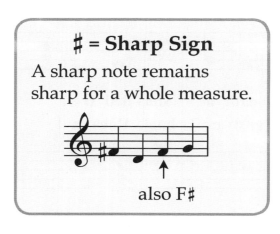

♯ = **Sharp Sign**

A sharp note remains sharp for a whole measure.

also F♯

LH 4 begins on ____.
RH 1 begins on ____.

Simple Gifts

Joseph Brackett

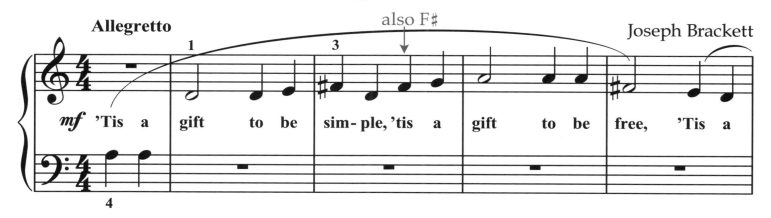

Allegretto

also F♯

mf 'Tis a gift to be sim-ple, 'tis a gift to be free, 'Tis a

ACCOMPANIMENT (Student plays one octave higher.)

mp with pedal

rit.

5

gift   to   come   down   where we ought to   be,   When

2   4

9

1

we   find our - selves   in the   place   just   right,   It will

13

be   in the   val - ley of   love   and de - light.

rit.

Drawing Sharps (♯) and Flats (♭)

The "square" in the middle of the sharp sign is placed **on a line** or **in a space**.

A. Draw a sharp sign (♯) in front of the note, then shade the matching key.

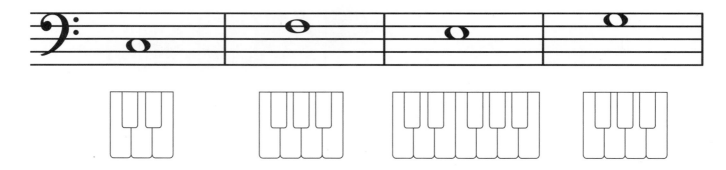

The "round" part of the flat sign is placed **on a line** or **in a space**.

B. Draw a flat sign (♭) in front of the note, then shade the matching key.

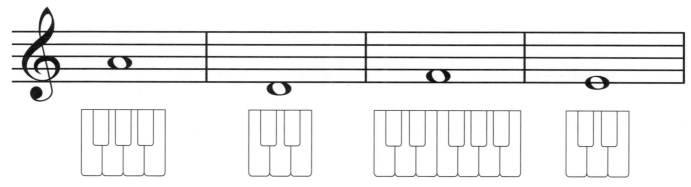

C. Shade the correct key.

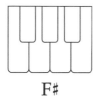

F♯

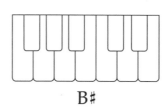

B♯

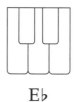

E♭

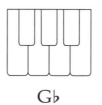

G♭

LH 3 begins on ___.
RH 1 begins on ___.

Little Spider

Allegretto

mf Lit - tle spi - der near my desk, I've got time to spend,

Play all LH chords softly

Spin your silk - y web right here, I will be your friend!

Lit - tle spi - der, lit - tle spi - der,

I will be your friend! Yes!

Stem Direction Review

Notes on or above the middle staff line have **down stems**.

Notes below the middle staff line have **up stems**.

Down Stems   **Up Stems**

Draw stems on these noteheads.

Trace clefs

LH 5 begins on ___.
RH 2 begins on ___.

Windy Night

Andante

2   3   3
1

mf - mp

Woke up   to   the | sound of branch-es | sway-ing back and | forth.

5

*Play both hands
8va higher on repeat*

5

Went out-side   to | feel the cold wind | blow-ing   on   my | ②porch.

LH over

Matching Terms

Draw lines connecting each term with its meaning.

Allegro	moderate
Andante	fast
Moderato	moderately fast
Allegretto	slowly (walking tempo)

RH 2 begins on ___.
LH 2 begins on ___.

Bouncy Balls

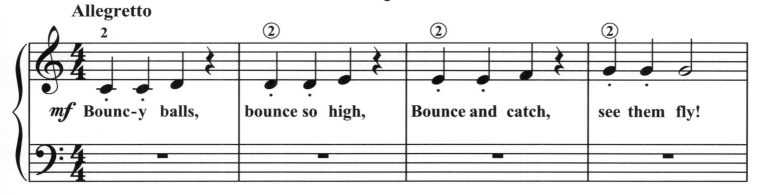

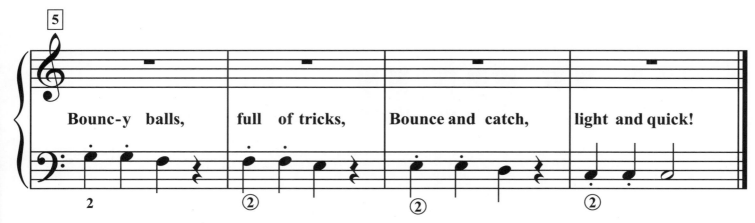

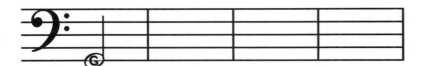

A. Draw each note three times.

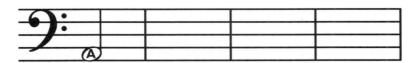

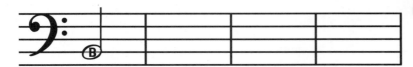

B. Name the notes.

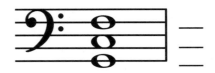

C. Name the notes.

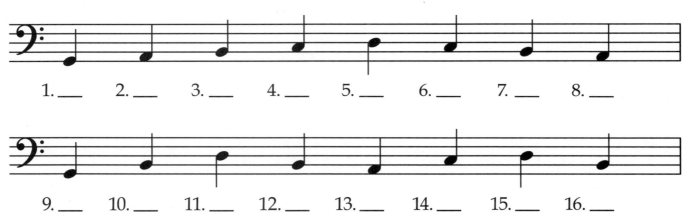

1. ___ 2. ___ 3. ___ 4. ___ 5. ___ 6. ___ 7. ___ 8. ___

9. ___ 10. ___ 11. ___ 12. ___ 13. ___ 14. ___ 15. ___ 16. ___

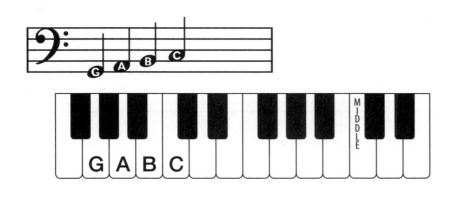

New Notes

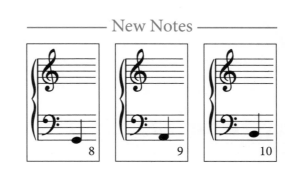

LH 5 begins on ___.
RH 1 begins on ___.

The Ostrich and Giraffe

Moderato

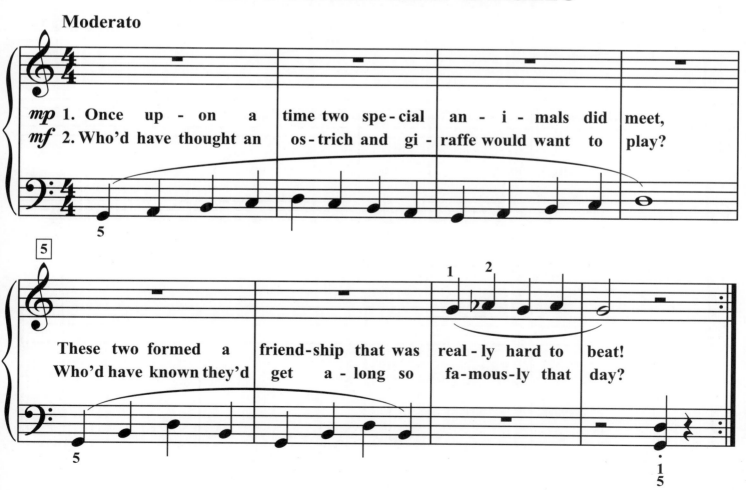

mp 1. Once up - on a time two spe - cial an - i - mals did meet,
mf 2. Who'd have thought an os - trich and gi - raffe would want to play?

5

These two formed a friend-ship that was real - ly hard to beat!
Who'd have known they'd get a - long so fa-mous-ly that day?

LH 5 begins on ___.

Long, Long Ago

Andante

Thomas H. Bayly

mf Tell me the tales that to me were so dear,

Long, long a - go, Long, long a - go,

Sing me the songs I de - light - ed to hear,

Play 8va lower to the end

Long, long a - go, long a - go.

Time for Theory

Accidentals are music symbols (♯, ♭) placed *before* notes to change them to become higher or lower notes.

When *naming* notes with accidentals, the ♯ or ♭ is placed *after* the letter name. (Examples: A♭ or C♯)

A. Name the notes.

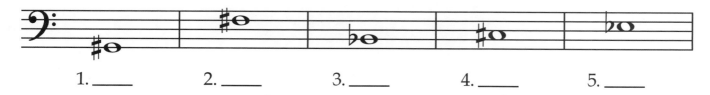

1. ____ 2. ____ 3. ____ 4. ____ 5. ____

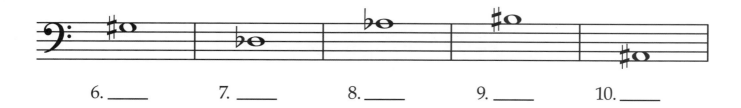

6. ____ 7. ____ 8. ____ 9. ____ 10. ____

B. Add notes or rests to complete these measures, then clap and count the rhythm aloud.

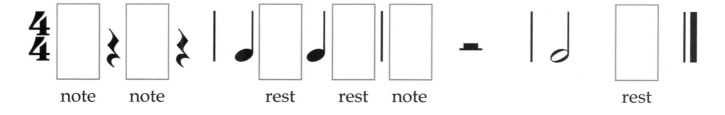

note note rest rest note rest

ACCOMPANIMENT for "Long, Long Ago"

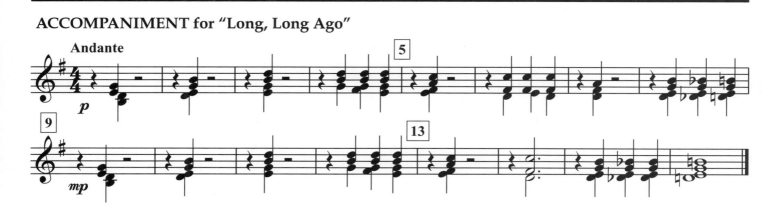

WP452

Octave Signs

8va = play one octave (8 notes) higher.

15ma = play two octaves (15 notes) higher.

RH 5 begins on ___.

RH 1 begins on ___.

LH 2 begins on ___.

Good King Wenceslas

Traditional Finnish Tune
Words by John M. Neale

Brightly shone the moon that night, tho' the frost was cruel, When a poor man came in sight, gath'ring winter fuel.

Time for Theory

A. Name the notes to form words.

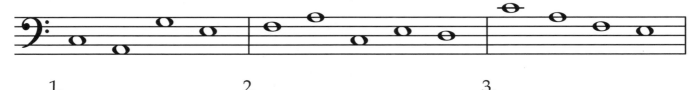

1. __ __ __ __   2. __ __ __ __ __   3. __ __ __ __

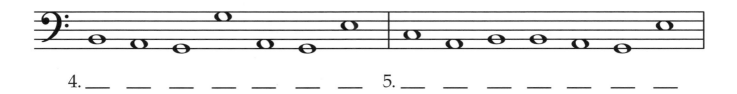

4. __ __ __ __ __   5. __ __ __ __ __ __

B. Name the interval (**2nd**, **3rd**, **4th**, or **5th**) in the box.

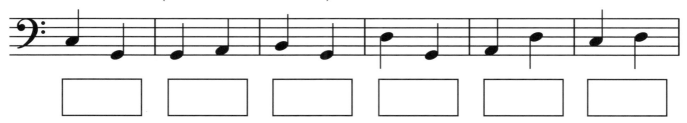

The LH plays the melody in *Circus Clowns*. As you play,
listen for a louder LH melody and a softer RH accompaniment.

LH 2 begins on ___.

RH 3 begins on ___.

RH 1 begins on ___.

Circus Clowns

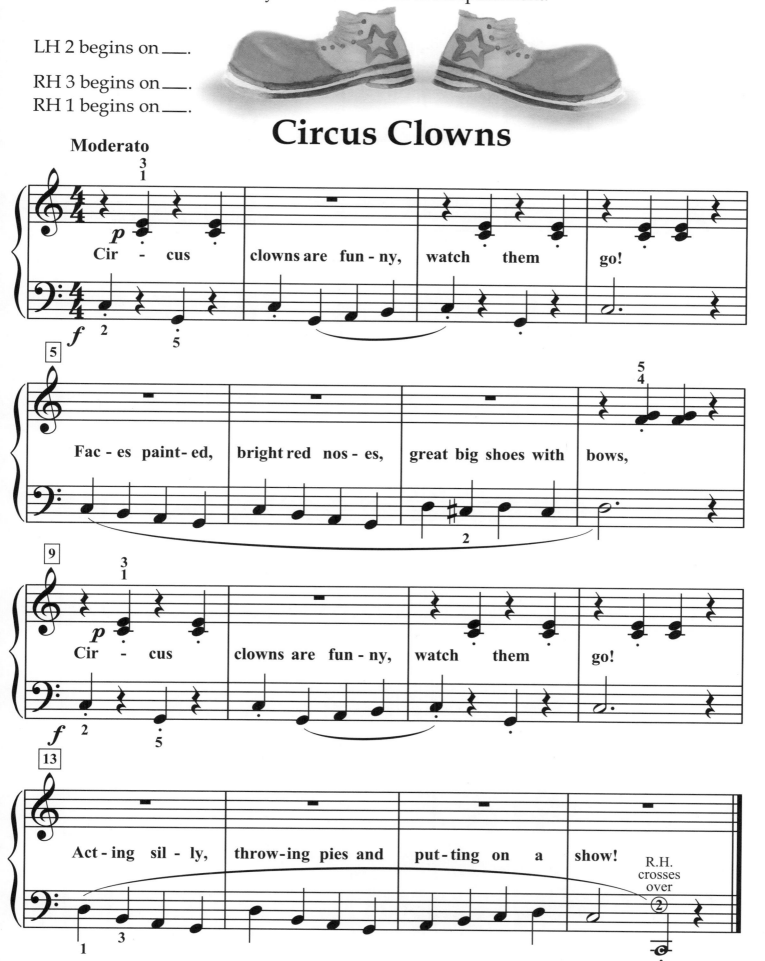

Moderato

Cir - cus   clowns are fun - ny,   watch   them   go!

Fac - es paint- ed,   bright red nos - es,   great big shoes with   bows,

Cir - cus   clowns are fun - ny,   watch   them   go!

Act - ing sil - ly,   throw - ing pies and   put - ting on a   show!

R.H. crosses over

𝄞 Line B 𝄞 Space C 𝄞 Line D

A. Draw each note three times.

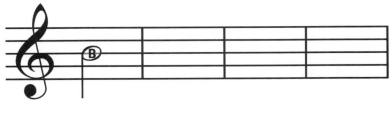

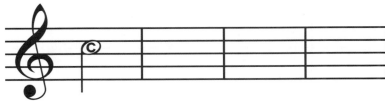

B. Name these guide notes.

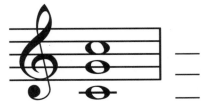

Treble C is another important guide note.

3rd space ©

C. Name the notes.

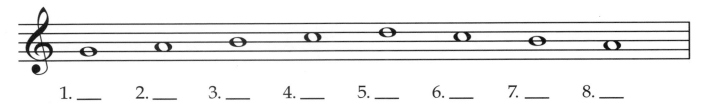

1. ___   2. ___   3. ___   4. ___   5. ___   6. ___   7. ___   8. ___

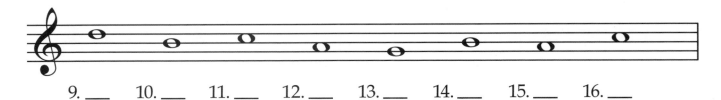

9. ___   10. ___   11. ___   12. ___   13. ___   14. ___   15. ___   16. ___

New Notes

31   32   33

G 5-Finger Position

All Day Hike

Moderato

mf Back-pack read-y, filled with wa-ter, nuts and rai-sins, too.

Hik-ing through the hills and trails is fun when I'm with you!

WP452

Matching Notes – Staff & Keyboard

1. Name these notes. Remember, the accidentals are written *after* the letters.
2. Write the number of each note on the matching key below.

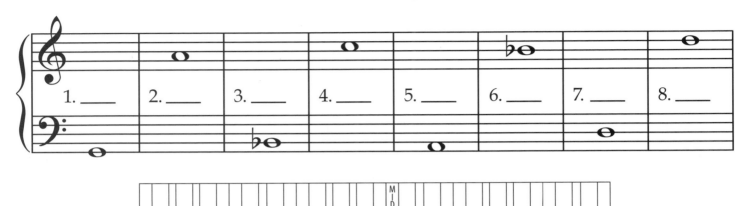

LH 5 begins on ___.
RH 3 begins on ___.

Hide and Seek

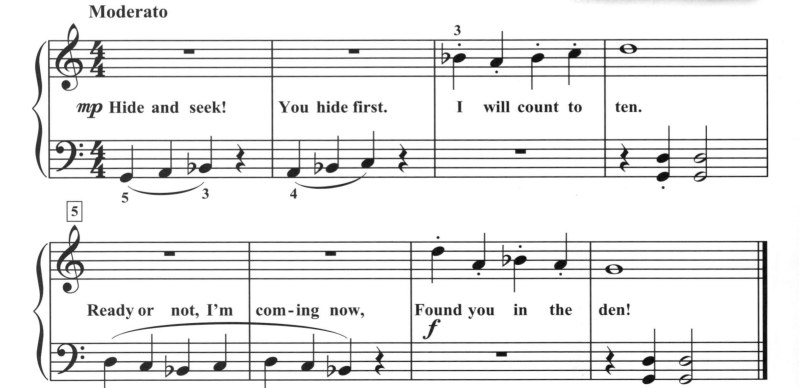

Moderato

mp Hide and seek! | You hide first. | I will count to | ten.

Ready or not, I'm | com-ing now, | Found you in the | den!

RH 1 begins on ___.

LH 1 begins on ___.
LH 5 begins on ___.

Bumper Cars

Allegretto

f Whis - tles blow! Start your en-gines, go!

I will run right in - to you, Noth-ing you can do!

Bum-per cars ig - nite, At the fair to - night.

8va

LH 3 begins on ___.

Turn and Spin

LH 5 begins on ___.
RH 5 begins on ___.

Thunder Boogie

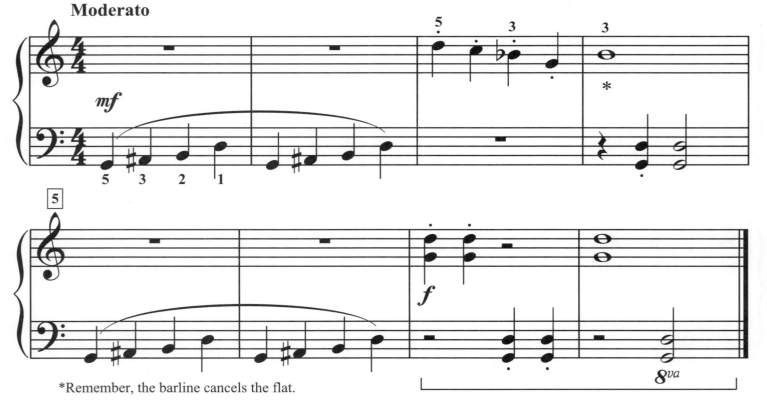

*Remember, the barline cancels the flat.

Name the notes to form words.

1. _____ _____ _____ _____

2. _____ _____ _____ _____ _____

3. _____ _____ _____ _____

RH 1 begins on ___.

LH 1 begins on ___.

LH 5 begins on ___.

Happy Monkeys

Moderato

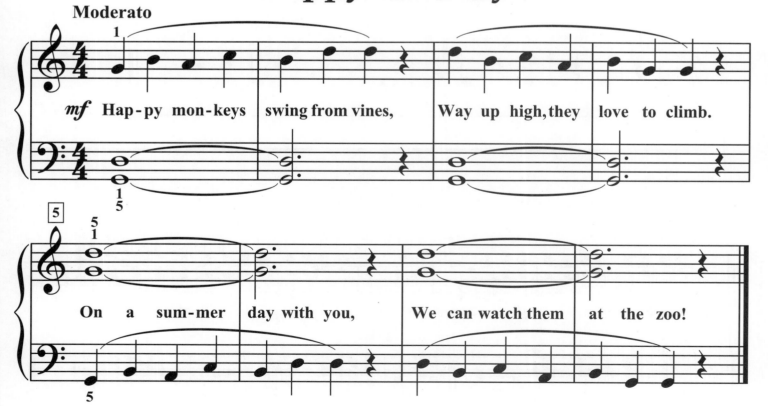

mf Hap-py mon-keys | swing from vines, | Way up high, they | love to climb.

On a sum-mer | day with you, | We can watch them | at the zoo!

Matching Notes – Staff & Keyboard

1. Name these notes. Remember, the accidentals are written *after* the letters.
2. Write the number of each note on the matching key below.

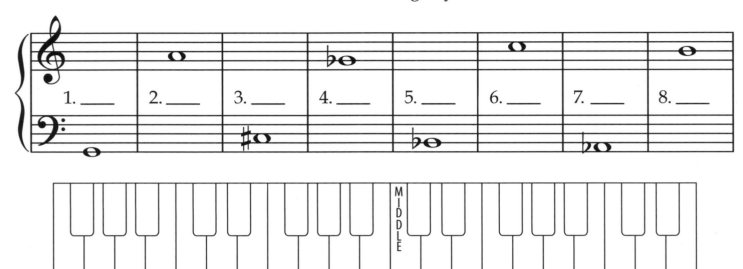

Rhythm Fun

Write the counts, then clap and count the rhythm aloud.

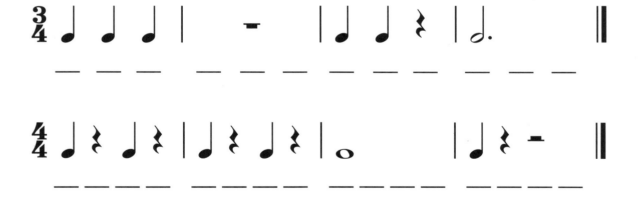

Spooky Noises
ACCOMPANIMENT (Student plays one octave higher.)

LH 4 begins on ___.
RH 1 begins on ___.

Spooky Noises

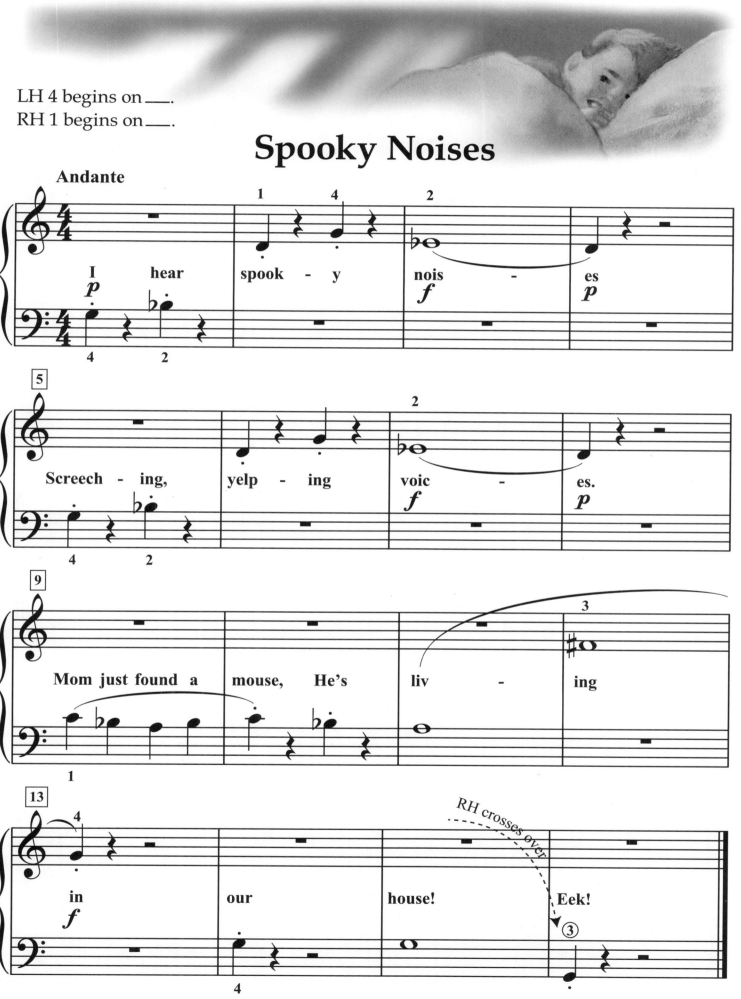

Andante

I hear spook - y nois - es

Screech - ing, yelp - ing voic - es.

Mom just found a mouse, He's liv - ing

in our house! Eek!

RH crosses over

LH 5 begins on ___.
RH 4 begins on ___.

Voices in Unison

Allegro

Based on "Easter Hymn"

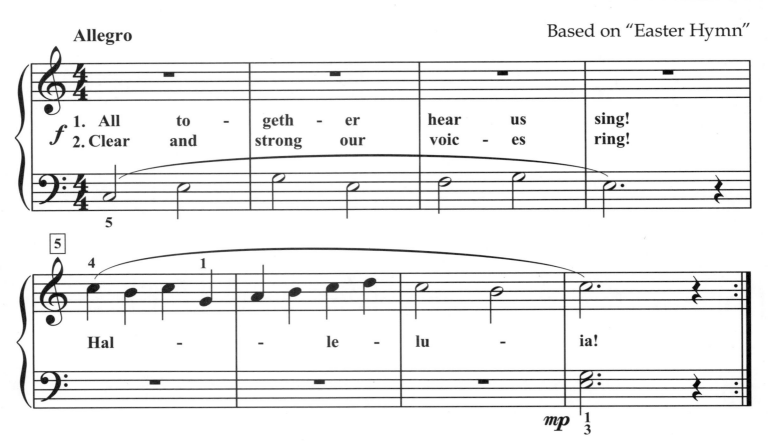

f

1. All to - geth - er hear us sing!
2. Clear and strong our voic - es ring!

5

5

4   1

Hal - - le - lu - ia!

mp 1 3

ACCOMPANIMENT (Student plays one octave higher.)

mf 2 5

5 3

2 5

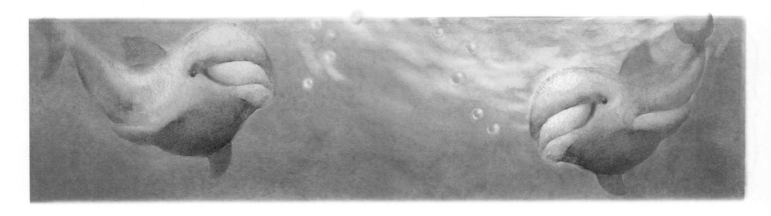

Time for Theory

A. Name each interval (**2nd**, **3rd**, **4th**, or **5th**), then play the notes on the piano.

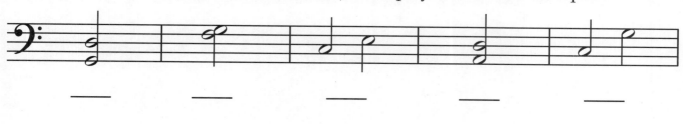

B. Fill in the pyramid with notes or rests so that each level is equal to four beats in $\frac{4}{4}$.

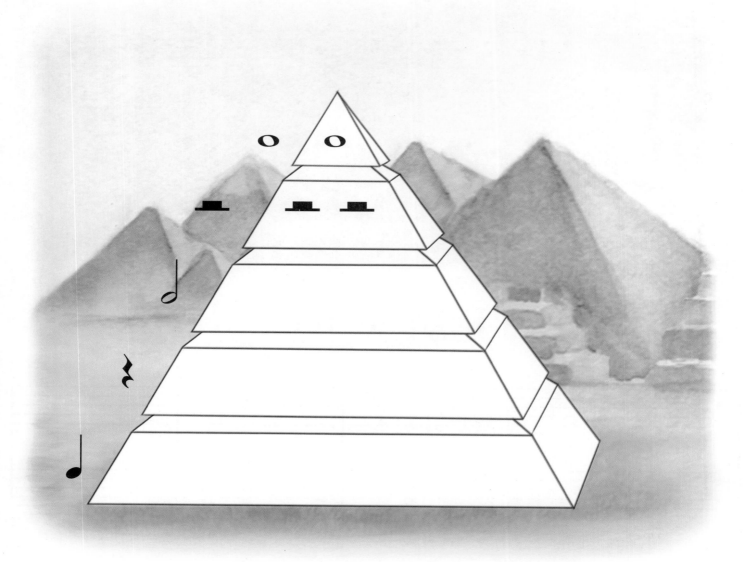

LH 1 begins on ＿＿.

LH 5 begins on ＿＿.

RH 5 begins on ＿＿.

Legends Told

Moderato

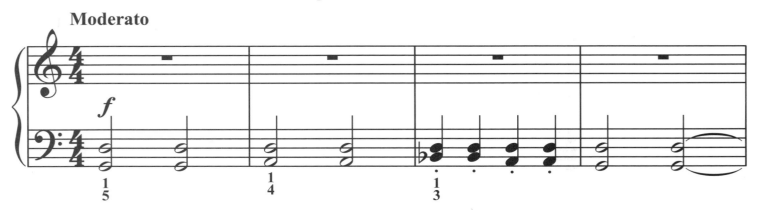

Frédéric Chopin, born in 1810, was a child prodigy from Poland who composed most of his music for the piano. His piece, *Fantasie-Impromptu*, was written in 1834 and is one of his most popular compositions.

Dynamics

Crescendo (*cresc.*)
Gradually play louder.

Diminuendo (*dim.*)
Gradually play softer.

RH 1 begins on ___.
LH 4 begins on ___.

Fantasie-Impromptu

Frédéric Chopin
(Arranged)

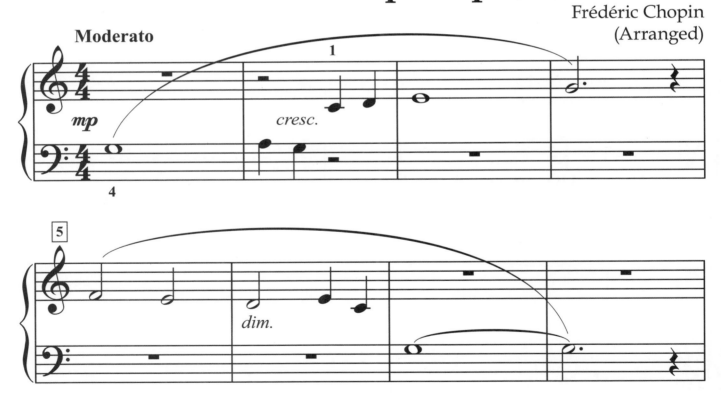

ACCOMPANIMENT (Student plays one octave higher.)

LH 1 begins on ___.
RH 1 begins on ___.

Notice the upbeat.

Aardvark Picnic

Moderato

mf An aard-vark said "My fav' rite thing would be a pic-nic in the spring, A

night time feast of ter-mite pie, un - der - neath the sky."

cresc.

Aard-vark pic - nic time!

8va

Kaleidoscope Colors

Color the notes and rests according to the counts they receive in $\frac{4}{4}$.

- 1 count = Red
- 2 counts = Blue
- 3 counts = Green
- 4 counts = Yellow

Take Me Out to the Ball Game

Music by Albert von Tilzer
Words by Jack Norworth

ACCOMPANIMENT (Student plays one octave higher.)

𝄢 Ledger Line D

A. Draw three D's.

B. Name these notes.

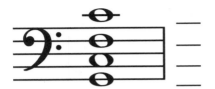

C. Name the notes.

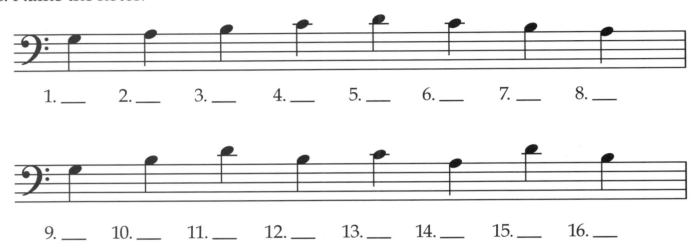

1. __ 2. __ 3. __ 4. __ 5. __ 6. __ 7. __ 8. __

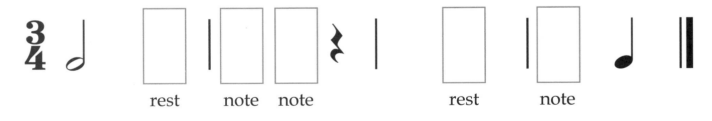

9. __ 10. __ 11. __ 12. __ 13. __ 14. __ 15. __ 16. __

Rhythm Review

Add notes or rests to complete these measures, then clap and count the rhythm aloud.

rest   note   note   rest   note

New Note

19

G 5-Finger Position

LH 3 begins on ___
RH 5 begins on ___

Under the Surf

Moderato

mf Way   down   low,   un - der-neath the surf,

Jel - ly - fish and her - mit crabs pro - tect their might - y turf. *mp*

RH 5 begins on ___.
LH 1 begins on ___.

Our Favorite Team

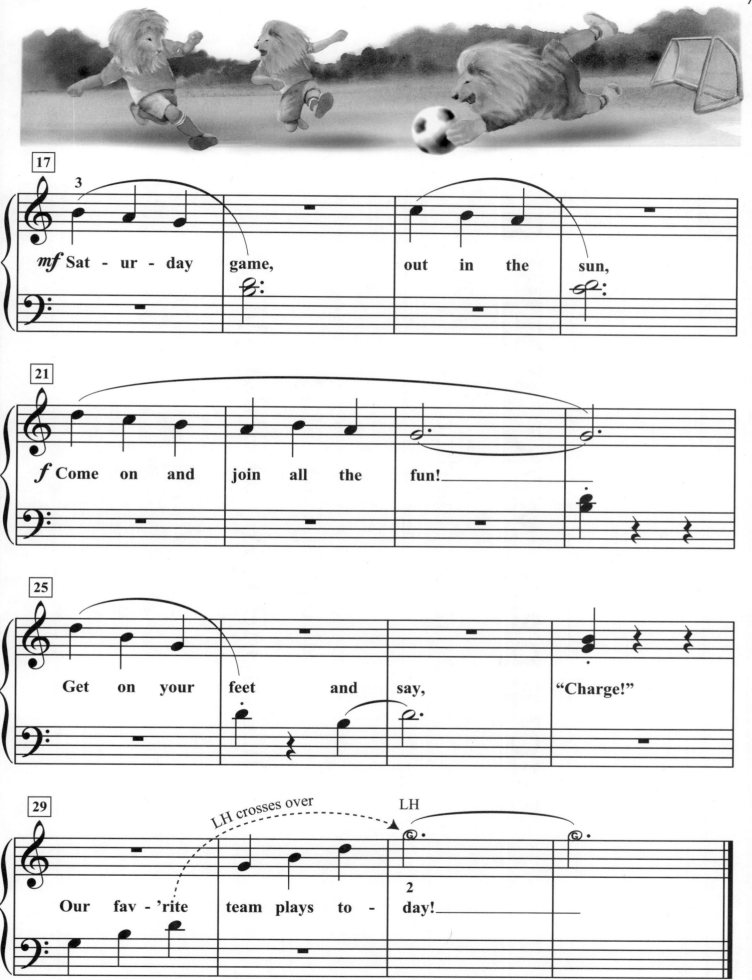

Certificate of Achievement

This certifies that

has completed Level 1A

of

Bastien® New Traditions

and is promoted to Level 1B.

This certificate is given in recognition of this significant achievement!

Teacher's Signature

Date